Brunel
in the West

Paul White

Bossiney Books

First published 2018 by
Bossiney Books Ltd, 67 West Busk Lane, Otley, LS21 3LY
www.bossineybooks.com
© 2018 Paul White   All rights reserved
ISBN 978-1-906474-66-9

Printed in Great Britain by R Booth Ltd, Penryn, Cornwall

*Brunel, standing in front of the SS Great Eastern at Millwall –
a remarkable photograph taken on location at a time when studio shots
were the norm*

Parents and childhood

Isambard Kingdom Brunel is perhaps the most famous, and he was certainly the most ambitious, British engineer of the 19th century and, although he made his home in London, he had a number of connections with the West Country.

His mother was born in Plymouth, Sophia Kingdom (1775-1855), youngest of the numerous children (probably sixteen) of William and Joan Kingdom of Stoke Damerel. William was a merchant who had contracts with the Navy. His will shows that he was an Anabaptist who supported Plymouth's Pigmarket Chapel, and at least nine of his children were well provided for in the will.

He died not long after Sophia's birth, and her elder brother, as her guardian, sent her to France as a governess to improve her French. Perhaps he had advanced political views – in the early days of the French Revolution there was a great deal of sympathy for it in Britain, but by 1792 rival revolutionary factions had turned against each other, and it was a dangerous time to be an English girl in Rouen. Sophia was arrested, and was probably lucky not to have been executed during 'The Terror'. Before her arrest she met Marc Isambard Brunel, a young French naval engineer.

Marc Brunel was a royalist, and was obliged to flee for his life to the USA, where he became engineer for New York City. After six years there, he came up with an idea for mechanising the production of 'blocks', the wooden pulleys vital to sailing ships. He recrossed the Atlantic, but to England not France, and was able to interest the Admiralty in his project. He also sought out Sophia and they were soon married, in 1799.

Marc became an enthusiastic British citizen, and before long he was writing his diaries in English rather than French. They had two daughters, and then in 1806 their only son, Isambard Kingdom Brunel. (For clarity I'll often refer to him as IKB, and his father, who preferred to be called Isambard, as Marc.)

IKB was born in Portsmouth, but the family soon moved to Chelsea. Marc taught the boy to draw accurately from the age of four, and to understand Euclid by the age of eight. Then IKB was sent to a boarding school in Hove, but with Europe at peace he went, at the age of fourteen, to France for his formal education at the Lycée Henri-

Quatre in Paris, and was then allowed to work for Louis Bréguet, a famous manufacturer of chronometers.

At that time, French mathematical education at school level was far superior to English, so when IKB returned, with that education and excellent work experience, he was way ahead of his contemporaries as a potential engineer – which was his own and his father's ambition for him. At that time, French engineers received a sound theoretical further education, whereas in Britain they began their careers as apprentices to craftsmen, who tended to be sensible and cautious.

Whilst the best French engineers then trained in the École Polytechnique, and the demand for their services mostly came from the military, in Britain, which was in the throes of the industrial revolution, innovation was in great demand from trade and industry.

IKB had the huge advantage of being brought up in both traditions, and would take innovation to extremes.

The Thames tunnel

While his son was in France, Marc Brunel was imprisoned for debt. He was a brilliant engineer, but a poor businessman; encouraged by the government but without a formal contract, he had developed at his own expense ideas such as a boot factory using mechanical tools (highly approved of by the Duke of Wellington, as one might expect) which lost money as soon as peace returned and the army didn't need boots.

A mild suggestion that he might accept an invitation to live and work in Russia quickly persuaded the government to buy him out of jail, and when IKB returned from France, he was able to begin working in his father's office on numerous and varied projects, from suspension bridges to marine steam engines. The division between civil engineers and mechanical engineers had not yet happened: it would occur in IKB's lifetime, but he resisted it – being convinced that he was to be *the* outstanding practitioner of both.

Marc Brunel's greatest achievement was a tunnel under the Thames between Wapping and Rotherhithe. River crossings were incredibly important, and there were far too few of them at most major ports: the problem was that sailing ships needed to reach the dock areas, and their masts were so tall that no bridge could be built which would not obstruct them. London Bridge was at the upper end of the dock area,

4

and by 1820 the riverside had been developed with docks, warehouses and housing for many miles downstream, but the north and south sides of the river were at best connected by passenger ferries.

The obvious answer was tunnelling, but the geology of the Thames river bed is such that the earliest tunnels, including one in which Richard Trevithick was involved, collapsed during construction and were never completed.

Marc Brunel, inspired by watching a teredo worm burrowing into wood, invented the tunnelling shield – a strong cylinder which could be inched forward as the tunnel progressed. The digging was all done by hand, and the conditions were atrocious, not helped by the fact that the Thames downstream from London Bridge was little better than a sewer, and its water inevitably seeped in – or occasionally threatened to surge in. As other managers became ill, and one died, IKB, at the age of 20, was promoted to resident engineer, effectively in charge of the work and supervising nearly 500 men, most of whom were either miners from Somerset or Irish navvies.

But in January 1828 there was a disaster which killed six workmen and very nearly killed Brunel. He described it in his diary, which alas he maintained only for a small part of his life:

> Here I am in bed at Bridge St. I have now been laid up quite useless for 14 weeks and upwards – ever since the 12th January. I shan't forget that day in a hurry. Very near finished my journey then. When the danger is over it is rather amusing than otherwise. While it existed I can't say the feeling was at all uncomfortable. If I was to say the contrary I should be nearer the truth in this instance. While exertions could still be made and hope remained of stopping the ground it was an excitement, which has always been a luxury to me. When we were obliged to run I felt nothing particular. I was only thinking of the best way of getting us on, and the probable state of the arches. When knocked down I certainly gave myself up but I took it very much as a matter of course which I had expected the moment we quitted the frames, for I never expected we should get out. The instant I disengaged myself and got breath again – all dark – I bolted into the other arch. This saved me. By laying hold of the rail rope – the engine must have stopped a minute – I stood still nearly a minute. I was anxious for poor

When the tunnel was finally completed, it became a tourist attraction

Ball and Collins who I felt too sure had never risen from the fall we all had – and were as I thought crushed under the great stage – I kept calling them by name to encourage them and make them also (if still able) come thro' the opening. While standing there the effect was grand – the roar of the rushing water in a confined passage and by its velocity rushing past the openings was grand very grand. I cannot compare it to anything – cannon can be nothing to it. At last it came bursting thro' the opening. I was then obliged to be off… Reaching the shaft I was too much bothered with my knee and some other thumps to remember much. If I had been kept under another minute when knocked down I should not have suffered more and I trust I was tolerably fit to die. If therefore the occurrence itself was rather a gratification than otherwise and the consequences in no way unpleasant I need not attempt to avoid such. My being in bed at present tho' no doubt arising from the effects of my straining was immediately caused by my returning too soon to a full diet at Brighton. Had I been properly warned of this I might now have been hard at work at the Tunnel.

The disaster was probably caused by Marc Brunel having being forced by the proprietors of the tunnel to make dangerous economies.

For the time being work ceased, and was not resumed for seven years, when the government lent money for the purpose, realising that the tunnel was essential for the national infrastructure. Marc Brunel completed it in 1843, and was knighted for his efforts.

The next Thames crossing

During the days of sail only one new bridge was constructed downstream from London Bridge – Tower Bridge, opened in 1894. IKB's second son Henry Marc Brunel was its structural engineer, in partnership with Sir John Wolfe Barry.

Bristol and Clifton

IKB, meanwhile, who would take no further part in the Thames tunnel project, was seriously ill with 'internal injuries' (which may have included a long-lasting infection from the sewage) as well as his damaged knee, and he convalesced, first at Brighton, probably with too much socialising causing a relapse, then with a brief trip to Plymouth, presumably to stay with his mother's relations, and then to Clifton near Bristol – a visit which would change his life.

He was out of work, with a CV including a tunnel which at that stage looked like a total disaster. And he had not recovered fully. Clifton was still a place for convalescence – though Hotwells, which had been very popular with invalids, was now less so, and Clifton was changing into an elegant suburb of the city. IKB soon made influential friends there.

One project which Bristolians had long thought desirable was a crossing of the Avon downstream from the city: it was needed for much the same reasons as the Thames Tunnel. A benefactor had left money for the purpose, and in 1829 there was a competition to design a bridge across the Clifton Gorge. Of the 22 designs entered, four were by Brunel, for different locations. The judge was the great engineer Thomas Telford, who had recently designed the Menai Straits suspension bridge.

Bristol in the early nineteenth century

Bristol had been an important port in the Middle Ages, but because of its western position became even more so with the development of trade with North America – and then the 'triangular' slave trade from which it benefited: sugar and tobacco were its key imports.

In the 18th century it had claims (never undisputed) to be Britain's second city. But a series of events reduced its importance – the American War of Independence, the abolition of the slave trade and the ever-growing industrial importance of the north of England.

In the early nineteenth century merchant ships were growing larger, and the port of Bristol, several miles from the sea, was less convenient than it had been. An ingenious but financially unwise improvement was made in the first decade by the creation of the 'floating harbour' – in essence a man-made lake separated by locks from the tidal flow of the River Avon. Because it had cost so much, the harbour dues were excessive.

Bristol's merchant families, wealthy from centuries of trade, were perhaps complacent. They also owned the lucrative harbour facilities and shipbuilding yards at the heart of the city, and were reluctant to abandon them or to invest in new facilities at Avonmouth. The port was steadily losing ground, particularly to Liverpool.

By 1830 there was also severe silting in the floating harbour, and there were powerful voices in Bristol arguing for change – at just the right time for Brunel.

Brunel wrote of this project that 'A work of art thus thrown across such grand and imposing scenery should be as simple and unobtrusive as possible, that it should fix the observer rather by the grandeur of the ideas that it gave rise to than attract his attention by anything inconsistent with the surrounding objects.' Which makes it hard to understand why his design included towers carved as Egyptian sphinxes. For reasons of economy, these never made it to the final version.

Telford, now over 70, rejected all the designs – including Brunel's

*Brunel's original design for the Clifton Suspension Bridge,
with Egyptian sphinxes for the towers*

on the grounds that no suspension bridge could possibly be safe if it
had a span of more than 600 ft (183 m) which was the length of the
span at his Menai Bridge. It is tempting to suspect that he didn't want
to be supplanted in the *Guiness Book of Records*, but he may well have
been right to be cautious.

The committee promptly asked Telford to submit his own design,
which he did. They accepted it, but it was ugly, and public opinion
objected. Fortunately it was also going to be too expensive, so the
acceptance was withdrawn politely on the grounds of cost and a new
competition announced, with Cornishman Davies Gilbert, President
of the Royal Society and a formidable mathematician, as judge.

This time IKB won the competition with a modified design, but only
after button-holing Davies Gilbert (they were socially acquainted)
to get the first choice candidate rejected. IKB rejoiced that 'Clifton
bridge – my first child, my darling' was begun: construction of the
massive abutments started in 1831 – but the money ran out, and riots
in Bristol meant the project was shelved.

Above: Bristol's 'floating harbour' as it is today, with the SS Great Britain as a major feature

Below: What remains of Brunel's 'swivel bridge' across the outer lock of the floating harbour

The riots were among the worst ever experienced in England. They seem to have been motivated by anger against the closed Corporation (a self-selecting and self-serving elite loathed even by Bristol's Chamber of Commerce) rather than being food riots, or in support of the Reform Bill. Many public and private buildings were burned down, and 12 rioters died.

The bridge project restarted in 1836, but soon stopped again for lack of cash. In the event Clifton Suspension Bridge was not built in Brunel's lifetime. After his death a group of admirers decided to proceed with it as a tribute to IKB, but they did so with the benefit of thirty more years of bridge-building experience. The Brunel family did not attend the opening ceremony in 1864: their absence was probably because they thought he should have been given sole credit for the bridge, with no mention of the engineers who had modified the design. Nowadays of course the opposite simplistic view is taken: the bridge is credited solely to Brunel, whereas if his design had been followed faithfully it might well have collapsed long before now.

The Bristol contacts IKB had established while working on the Clifton Suspension Bridge were to prove hugely important. Firstly his advice was sought for the improvement of the floating harbour. He suggested a dredger, new lock gates and sluice gates. Some but not all of his proposals were put into effect at the time, and he designed a new entrance lock in 1844. All his suggestions for a new port at Avonmouth or Portishead fell on deaf ears.

The Great Western Railway

While IKB was in Bristol awaiting a decision about his plans for the docks, he was approached by what would become the GWR, and in 1833 became their engineer. He was a man of extraordinary vision. Instead of thinking in terms of a goods railway between Bristol and London, or a meandering line that would join up as many sleepy market towns as possible, Brunel's vision was for something more like an HST line. Irritated by the shaking of the carriage when travelling at 28mph on the newly opened Liverpool & Manchester Railway, he wrote:

> The time is not far off when we shall be able to take our coffee and write while going, noiseless and smoothly, at 45 miles per hour … let me try.

The line he envisaged and surveyed, from London to Bristol, was to be a trunk route. And at an early meeting of the board it was suggested, some say by Brunel, others by the businessman T R Guppy, and whether initially as a joke is unclear, that the London to Bristol line be extended to New York, by way of a steamship service from the port of Bristol. That idea was taken up with enthusiasm. The story of the great steam ships IKB designed runs simultaneously with his railway and bridge-building activities, but for simplicity it will be covered separately later in this book.

The route Brunel surveyed for the GWR was extraordinary for its flatness. Drive the M4 from London to Bristol today and you won't think it mountainous, but there are undoubtedly some hills. A motorway can have a gradient as steep as 1 in 25, but gradients are much more of a problem for railways. The first 67 miles of Brunel's line to Bristol are never steeper than 1 in 1320 and the remaining 47 miles no steeper than 1 in 660. It was an astonishing achievement, described as 'Brunel's billiard table'.

Negotiations with landowners were conducted by Brunel, and when the Bill to allow the line was presented to Parliament it was Brunel who faced 11 days of hostile cross-examination. There were many objections, and after 56 days in Committee the Bill failed. It was resubmitted soon after, with modifications, and despite the continued objections of Eton College (its pupils might be able to visit the bright lights and dark corners of London), of country landowners, and of 'scientists' who were convinced that the noise would drive passengers mad if two trains passed each other in the Box Tunnel, it was passed.

One little fact Brunel artfully omitted from the GWR's parliamentary Bill was that he proposed to use a 7 ft gauge, in contrast to the 'standard gauge' used by all the other new railways: IKB believed this would enable his trains to run faster and more smoothly, and in the short run they did, but the competing gauges would in time turn out to be something of a disaster.

A national railway system needs a unified gauge. He had perhaps expected that the success of the broad gauge would force all other railways to recognise his genius, and follow suit – and the company hoped to achieve a total monopoly in southern Britain – but neither happened. Broad gauge was finally scrapped overnight in 1892.

Work started from both ends, and Brunel tried to be everywhere at

The interior of Bristol Temple Meads station as it first appeared

once. He often used a *britska*, a long horse-drawn carriage in which he could accommodate a bed, a drawing board and a huge cigar case: IKB chain-smoked cigars throughout his career.

To describe Brunel as a workaholic would be an understatement. One of his assistants wrote:

> I never met his equal for sustained power of work. After a hard day spent in preparing and delivering evidence, and after a hasty dinner, he would attend consultations till a late hour; and then, secure against interruption, sit down to his papers, and draw specifications, write letters or reports, or make calculations all through the night. If at all pressed for time he slept in his armchair for two or three hours, and at early dawn he was ready for the work of the day. When he travelled he usually started about four or five in the morning, so as to reach his ground by daylight. His travelling carriage, in which he often slept, was built from his own design, and was a marvel of skill and comfort. This power of work was no doubt aided by the abstemiousness of his habits and by his light and joyous temperament. One luxury, tobacco, he indulged in to

excess, and probably to his injury. At all times, even in bed, a cigar was in his mouth; and wherever he was engaged, there, near at hand, was the enormous leather cigar-case so well known to his friends, and out of which he was quite as ready to supply their wants as his own.

At times he worked 20 hours a day. He was all but incapable of delegation, and fired off a continuous stream of letters to subordinates. As for workmen and contractors, they were treated in an appalling manner, with money witheld on account of delays, even when the cause of the delay was bad weather, or sometimes Brunel's own fault. Many of his contractors went bankrupt as a result.

The 'North Star', a Robert Stephenson model locomotive, adapted for the GWR's broad gauge

Even more problematic was his refusal to co-operate with other engineers: he had to be in sole charge, not least so that nobody should share the fame he expected to generate.

As the construction work proceeded at great pace, Brunel's energies were required for its supervision, but at the same time for the preliminary work on extension lines and branch lines, including the Bristol & Exeter Railway, not to mention his first steamship and continuing dock work both at Bristol and at Monkwearmouth near Sunderland.

On the London-Bristol line the most challenging site was the 1.8 mile (nearly 3 km) Box Tunnel between Chippenham and Bath, which many had thought impossible when it was proposed. Lighting was by candles, and a tonne of candles as well as a tonne of explosives were used each week. To save time, and therefore money, blasting took place while men were in the tunnel. About a hundred men died in the operation, and at least 130 were hospitalised. Brunel thought this wasn't too bad, given the problems of construction. He was not nicknamed 'the reckless engineer' without cause. His attitude to safety, in which he was not alone at that time, was that accidents were inevitable. The most that can be said in his defence is that he subjected himself, and even at times visiting friends and family, to similar high risks.

The first trains began running in 1838, from London to Maidenhead. Various manufacturers had made the locomotives. Brunel had, of course, drawn up the specifications himself – but he had made serious mistakes. His locomotives not only looked ridiculous, with their 10 ft driving wheels: from the start they caused major problems, being short on power and liable to break down.

The only locomotive that worked well was the *North Star*, which was a Robert Stephenson model adapted for broad gauge.

Fortunately for the GWR, and for Brunel, he had employed a young northerner called Daniel Gooch as his Chief Locomotive Assistant, and Gooch knew what he was doing. He was able to improve some of the new locomotives by modifications, though quite soon 'Brunel's freaks' had to be replaced. Naturally IKB blamed Gooch for not taking the blame himself.

And it was not only the freaks. One friend of Brunel's wrote in his private diary:

> With all his talent he has shown himself deficient, I confess, in general arrangement; I mean in arranging his work in his own

The original frontage of Bristol Temple Meads station

mind so as to enable him to proceed with it rapidly,
economically and surely. There have been too many
mistakes: too much of doing and undoing.

Working 20 hours a day and failing to delegate is a mistake even
for a genius, and the folly of building railways with different gauges
was already obvious. There were calls for Brunel to be sacked, but he
survived. The total achievement outweighed the mistakes, though
admittedly the cost was nearly three times Brunel's original estimate.

The line was fully open to Bristol in 1841, and indeed to Bridgwater,
because the allied Bristol & Exeter Railway, also with Brunel as
Engineer, had progressed that far. By 1845, expresses were timetabled
to run the 194 miles from Exeter to London in $4^{1}/_{2}$ hours, which com-
pared to $16^{1}/_{2}$ by the fastest coach.

It is hard now to understand the effect the railway had on a county
like Devon, hitherto largely dependent on the sea for its connection
with the capital. But the connection of London with Plymouth and
then with Cornwall (which already had some railways of its own) was
still to be achieved. The South Devon Railway, for which Brunel was
yet again Engineer, was soon to follow – though not without major
problems.

The atmospheric disaster

Whilst the country between London, Bristol and Exeter is not totally flat, Brunel had been able to produce a line with surprisingly level gradients. There was no way that could be achieved on the South Devon Railway, certainly not beyond Newton Abbot.

The coastal route as far as Teignmouth, then inland, was a good start, though even today it is a nightmare to its operators due to regular damage by the sea. From Newton Abbot to Plymouth, however, there was no avoiding the hills.

Ever on the lookout for new ideas, Brunel seized on a new device, the atmospheric system. This was not Brunel's invention, but along with most other railway engineers he had seen it demonstrated on a short line rising out of Dún Laoghaire (then known as Kingstown). And he was not alone in being impressed. The eminent engineer Sir William Cubitt experimented with the system on the London to Croydon Railway.

Instead of locomotives, there were to be stationary engine houses at intervals along the line. These pumped air out of a continous cylinder between the tracks, forming a partial vacuum. A lightweight trolley was fitted to each train, with a piston inside the cylinder, and the vacuum pulled the train along the tracks.

This system had great attractions, and had enthusiastic public and political support. It is easy for us to romanticise steam locomotives, which today we only experience running at slow speeds in nostalgic settings. In fact they were dirty, noisy, and liable to cause fires along the line, due to sparks and hot cinders being raked out. Everyone (except Robert Stephenson, who was passionate about steam locomotives) hoped for something better.

Moreover, the locomotives were heavy: Daniel Gooch's experiments showed that, at 60mph, no less than half the power generated by the locomotive was needed to move the weight of the locomotive itself, and this problem increased the steeper the gradient. The atmospheric system meant that trains could be much lighter, and so cope far better with gradients. And if trains were lighter, and ran more smoothly, then the bridges, viaducts and permanent way could all be built more cheaply, and more direct routes could be chosen because the gradient issue would be less important.

The atmospheric engine house at Starcross, topped by a flag

The enthusiasts insisted that both initial costs and running costs would be lower. And Brunel joined the enthusiasts, telling the South Devon Railway:

> It appears to me also that the quality of the travelling will be much improved; that we shall attain greater speed, less noise and motion, and an absence of the coke dust, which is certainly still a great nuisance; and an inducement will thus be held out to those (the majority of travellers) who travel either solely for pleasure, or at least not from necessity, and who are mainly influenced by the degree of comfort with which they can go from place to place.
>
> Lastly, the average cost of working the trains will be much less than by locomotives....
>
> I have no hesitation in taking upon myself the full and entire responsibility for recommending the adoption of the atmospheric system on the South Devon Railway and of recommending as a consequence that the line and works should be constructed for a single line only.

The line from Exeter to Teignmouth took a long time to construct and was expensive, not least because Brunel started with pipes of 13 inch diameter, then decided to scrap them and substitute 15 inch pipes, but it was worked by the atmospheric system from September 1847, and from January 1848 this was extended to Newton Abbot. Seven months later it was obvious even to Brunel that the system was a disaster. All future working of the line would be by locomotives. Cubitt's Croydon line had already despaired of the system.

Part of the problem was that the pumping engines were underpowered, but also that they had to be kept running when there was no train to be pulled, then were suddenly expected to operate at full capacity for a minute or two. They often broke down, and when that happened it brought the entire line to a halt.

But the underlying problem was that the train's piston entered the vacuum cylinder through a slit. This was kept shut by a long leather strip reinforced by metal – and very soon the leather began to deteriorate. Freezing conditions, summer sun, salt water from spray, all had an effect. There is a legend that rats were partial to the wax which was used as a sealant, and this might even be true. For a full account of the problems on the SDR, and a no-punches-pulled assessment of Brunel's mismanagement and even misconduct, read Adrian Vaughan's book (see book list on page 32).

There are three surviving engine houses, of which that at Starcross was the only one to operate. Those at Totnes and at Torquay (the SDR had a branch as far as Torre) were built but the system was abandoned before they came into use.

Daniel Gooch in his memoirs wrote: 'I could not understand how Mr Brunel could be so misled. He had so much faith in his being able to improve it that he shut his eyes to the consequence of failure.' Brunel was a visionary, with extraordinary self-confidence.

Perhaps we might compare the attraction of the atmospheric system to the possibilities of the self-driving electric car back in 2010: every car manufacturer must look to the future, but (even at the time of writing in 2017) it would be a bold manufacturer who immediately ceased their existing production and made only self-driving electric vehicles. Brunel was that bold: it was an eggs-in-one-basket case. The investors in the SDR lost their money.

Nevertheless, he was not fired.

The line from Exeter as far as Teignmouth ran, and still runs, perilously near the coast. This is Dawlish station.

From Newton Abbot to Plymouth the line had been planned for the atmospheric system, so it has quite steep gradients, and also some fine viaducts especially that at Ivybridge.

The Cornwall Railway and the Royal Albert Bridge

Viaducts are also a feature of the Cornwall Railway, a company which originally intended a route from the port of Falmouth to London. It was able to collaborate with other lines which already existed – Cornwall having been, through Murdoch and Trevithick, and the requirements of the mining industry, a pioneer county in the development of steam traction.

The West Cornwall Railway's Hayle-Redruth line was extended at either end, to Penzance and to Truro, thus linking with the Cornwall Railway – though there was a change of gauge at Truro.

The Cornwall Railway crossed so many valleys running south to the sea that there were, in the 53 miles from Saltash to Truro, 34 viaducts totalling over five miles in length. The company was chronically short of money, not least because the 'railway mania' financial bubble had burst; the line was only made possible by Brunel's extraordinarily economical timber viaducts: these looked so flimsy that some people didn't dare use the railway in case they collapsed. It was deliberate short-term planning, and it was understood that each viaduct would need replacing when money allowed. This happened slowly, between 1871 and 1904.

The greatest visible achievement of this line was, however, the crossing of the Tamar by the Royal Albert Bridge.

Brunel had by this time designed many bridges, of all kinds of construction including masonry or brick arches (such as the Maidenhead Bridge featured in Turner's famous painting 'Rain, Steam and Speed'), lattice girders and suspension bridges, but the Royal Albert Bridge was innovatory, though his earlier bridge over the Wye at Chepstow had shared some of its characteristics.

Consider a 'standard' suspension bridge, such as the one at Clifton. The roadway hangs from the long 'chains' stretching from tower to tower. Left to itself, the roadway would drop, pulling the towers inward towards each other, but this is prevented by connecting the top of each tower to a firm anchorage on the landward side, keeping the tower upright. In the Tamar bridge, the tendency of the towers to topple towards each other is, instead, prevented by the huge tubular wrought-iron arch. All the stresses of the bridge are contained within its own length, leaving the lengthy viaduct at the Saltash side completely unaffected.

The crossing would not have been possible if there had not been a rocky outcrop underwater in mid-stream, upon which with great ingenuity an iron tube was fitted upright, forming the central pier. The two central trusses were, one by one, floated out into position until they rested on the piers, then lifted three feet at a time by hydraulic jacks, and the piers built up beneath them. It was a process that took many months for each truss, and for once Brunel seems to have been happy to leave much of the work to an assistant engineer, Robert Pearson Brereton. After Brunel's death, Brereton carried on his business, completing the Cornwall Railway, the West Somerset Railway and the Dartmouth & Torbay Railway, the latter two now surviving, and thriving, as preserved lines.

The Royal Albert Bridge from the Plymouth side

The Act allowing construction of the bridge was passed in 1846, but it took a long time to build, for reasons both structural and financial. The opening was by Prince Albert on 2 May 1859, though Brunel was too ill to attend. But he did see his great bridge before his death, later that year: a special train carried him slowly across the bridge, lying on a couch in a waggon.

With the railway now continuous between Penzance and London, whole new industries came into being. Cornwall's mild winters meant that vegetables, not to mention daffodils, could be grown earlier in the year than elsewhere, and now they could be at Covent Garden the night they were picked. The fishing industry benefitted too. And in the opposite direction there was the opportunity for the tourist industry to develop, though that was a slower process.

The gauge war

From very early on, objections were raised to the GWR using a gauge of 7 ft 0¼ in (2.14 m) when most other railways were using 4 ft 8½ in (1.435 m). Brunel's early reasoning for the broad gauge was that the bodies of rolling stock would be able to rest between the wheels, and thereby have a lower centre of gravity which would enable faster speeds, but this was soon found impracticable.

Tested against each other, a broad gauge locomotive proved to be considerably faster than a 'narrow gauge' competitor, but this probably had more to do with the superior design of Gooch's locomotive than with the gauge. It is hard to escape the feeling that Brunel *knew* broad gauge must be better simply because that was what he Brunel had chosen, and sooner or later the competition would have to submit to his greater genius. Robert Stephenson meanwhile confessed that with hindsight he would have chosen something a few inches wider, but not broad gauge.

A major division soon became clear between 'narrow gauge' and 'broad gauge' companies, and each side hoped to become totally dominant in its own geographical area, but the disadvantages became ever more obvious as the railway network grew, and more interchanges were required. In the south-west there was huge rivalry between the GWR and the LSWR. Broad gauge was doomed to lose the argument as soon as the government saw the need for national standardisation, because there was eight times as much track laid to 4 ft 8 1/2 in as there was to broad gauge, and any technical superiority was by that time very marginal.

An Act of 1846 decreed that 'narrow gauge' would in future be 'standard gauge', and any new railway must be built to that. For a time some lines had 'mixed gauge', with three rails instead of two, but in 1892 the whole broad gauge system was converted.

Broad gauge locomotives at Bath station

Two great steamships

As if building 1200 miles of railway were not enough, Brunel was simultaneously involved with other projects, most notably the construction of ever larger steam vessels. The SS *Great Western* was his first, a timber-hulled paddle steamer of 2300 tons designed as a transatlantic passenger vessel. Steam vessels had crossed the Atlantic since 1819, but none of them were on this scale, or designed for a regular service. And they were really sailing ships which used their engines only when there was no wind – they could not carry enough coal for a continuous crossing under steam.

The SS *Great Western* was launched in 1837 and sailed to London to have its engines fitted. She had just started down the Thames on the return journey when there was a fire on board, which was very nearly disastrous. In the confusion, Brunel tried to descend to the engine room, but the rungs of the ladder had charred and they broke under his weight. He fell 20ft (6m), and was very fortunate to land on top of the captain, but then lay unconscious on a flooded floor. Fortunately the captain was uninjured, saw a body in the flood and, not knowing who it was, had him pulled up to safety. Brunel was seriously hurt and spent three weeks in bed.

Without Brunel on board, the *Great Western* made what would have been the first continuous steam crossing of the Atlantic, except that the little *Sirius* had beaten her to it. But it was a Pyrrhic victory: the *Sirius* had taken longer, had used every bit of space for coal and had no coal left, whereas the *Great Western* still had fuel to spare. The ship proved commercially successful, making 67 crossings in eight years.

A sister ship was called for, but naturally Brunel didn't want a sister ship, he wanted something bigger and better. At first he was thinking timber, but before long he envisaged a cast-iron paddle steamer: the keel was laid in 1839, and the engines ordered. Then the *Archimedes*, the only screw-propelled ship in the world, arrived in Bristol, and Brunel was hugely impressed. Work on the paddle

> Some of Brunel's activities fall well outside the scope of this book, not just assistance with railway building in Italy, India and Australia, but contributions to the Great Exhibition and the design of a prefabricated hospital for the Crimea.

The SS Great Britain, rescued from the Falklands in 1970 and brought back to Bristol, where she had been built

engines must stop immediately, we need an engine for a propeller instead! Francis Humphrys, the engineer designing the engines, was already stressed – working for Brunel was no joke – and receiving this instruction he had a stroke and died a few days later.

Work on the new ship stopped for two years while Brunel, with, for once, a little cooperation from the Admiralty, worked out how to proceed. He designed an incredibly efficient propeller, and by 1843 the SS *Great Britain* was launched into Bristol's floating dock. And there she stayed. The dock company had failed to live up to its promise to widen their entrance lock, and the ship was trapped.

In the end, part of the lock wall was temporarily removed and she escaped. Rival port Liverpool must have been giggling as Bristol self-destructed. Even the SS *Great Britain*, owned by the Bristolian Great Western Steamship Company, would need to be based at Liverpool rather than Bristol.

Stephen Brindle wrote 'She is arguably the single most important vessel, in terms of ship design, in history' and it is hard to disagree. She made her first Atlantic crossing in 14 days, 15 days return, and all looked rosy. Then on her fifth trip she ran onto a sandbank in Dundrum Bay as a result of a navigational blunder which remains mysterious: was there a chart error? did the captain mistake which lighthouse he had seen? or was it the result of the iron hull affecting the ship's compass in a way not then understood?

Whatever the cause, it was not Brunel's fault. The ship's owners would probably have left her there, expecting her to break up as a timber ship would have done, but Brunel bullied them into defending the wreck from the sea with a temporary breakwater, and then into salvaging her. After such a publicity disaster, she was never going to be a success as a passenger liner. She was converted into a steam powered clipper which sailed the Australia run for many years, then served as a floating warehouse in the Falklands. In 1970 she was rescued, and brought back to Bristol where today she is a superb memorial to Isambard Kingdom Brunel.

Brunel's private life, London and Torquay

Much of Brunel's socialising seems to have been an extension of his professional career, being a member of the Royal Society, fraternising with fellow professionals such as Charles Babbage, and as many of the great and the good as he could meet, but he enjoyed musical soirées hosted by the Horsley family, also enthusiastically attended by Felix Mendelssohn. In 1836, by which time he was financially successful, Brunel married Mary Horsley, renowned for her beauty and also known within her family as a great domestic organiser.

They lived at 18 Duke Street, Westminster, above his professional offices, and in time added the next-door house as part of their home. Both of them enjoyed the wealth the business created, and were enthusiastic purchasers of paintings, furniture, Indian carpets and lavish clothes for Mary. Fortunately neither seems to have minded too much about their frequent separations while IKB rushed about the country. They had three children, Isambard who became an ecclesiastical lawyer, Henry Marc who became a structural engineer and helped design London's Tower Bridge, and Florence Mary who married an Eton schoolmaster.

Surprisingly, from 1842 if not earlier Brunel found time for an annual family holiday, though as was normal with busy men in the Victorian period he himself would often head back to his London

Watcombe Park, Torquay, alias Brunel Woods, where Brunel spent many years developing woodland and gardens, but never actually built the house. Today it is an attractive woodland area and the site of 'Brunel's Dance' – a group of wooden statues carved in his honour

office while leaving the family by the seaside, at Weston-super-Mare in 1842, Clevedon in 1843, and then from 1847 in Torquay.

There is no doubt that Brunel was doing well financially. In 1846-7, a year when income tax was temporarily imposed, Brunel declared an income after expenses of £24,000, a huge sum in those days.

The successful Victorian merchant or professional man often had aspirations to retire as a member of the landed gentry, and Brunel followed that pattern. In 1847 he bought land at Watcombe on the outskirts of Torquay with a view to building a country house – though one of the designs he came up with looked more like a French chateau.

Brunel's brother-in-law the artist John Callcott Horsley and his family also spent time nearby at their own house, which is now Orestone Manor Hotel.

The estate Brunel bought can be visited as a woodland park. Brunel was intensely happy planning the planting of trees. Sadly perhaps, the house – now intended to be an Italianate villa – was never built, except for its foundations, and the Brunels never lived there, though they continued to make regular visits. This was probably because Brunel often accepted all or part of his fee for a project not in cash but in shares in the business, which was perhaps unwise.

Whilst Brunel was a phenomenal engineering innovator, quite often the result of being first to create something is fame but not profit – and Brunel was always liable to underestimate either the production cost or the risks involved. The Editor of the *Railway Times* wrote:

> We do not take him for either a rogue or a fool but an enthusiast, blinded by the light of his own genius, an engineering knight-errant, always on the look-out for magic caves to be penetrated and enchanted rivers to be crossed, never so happy as when engaged 'regardless of cost' in conquering some, to ordinary mortals, impossibility.

The SS Great Eastern

The next great ship was built on the Thames and designed for trade with the Far East and Australia, so it might not have been covered at all in this book, except that it was such a financial disaster for Brunel that he was in no position to complete the Watcombe house.

The rationale for 'the great ship' was that it would be large enough to carry coal for the whole trip, and even for the return journey. Coal was relatively cheap and easy to obtain in British ports, but in other parts of the world there might be no convenient coal seams, and if there was as yet no manufacturing industry demanding coal, there would be no substantial coal supply.

Naturally Brunel's visionary approach, not to mention his desire to make the biggest and best, drew him into the project. And it was indeed to be a great ship, 692ft (211m) long and 18,915 tons, with both paddles and a screw propeller, and 4000 passenger berths.

The problems that bedevilled the building of the ship included a lack of teamwork between Brunel and the highly experienced ship-builder John Scott Russell, unchecked theft of materials from the shipyard, the bankruptcy of Russell, the decision to launch the vessel sideways rather than the conventional stern first method, and not least the huge publicity which this extraordinary project generated.

Londoners came in droves, especially to the launch attempts, where the directors angered Brunel by selling tickets for 3000 people to watch the launch from inside the shipyard, and not giving him enough time to make proper arrangements.

The first launch attempt failed but the second attempt, using powerful hydraulic jacks produced by the Cornish Tangye brothers, succeeded on 31 January 1858.

By this time the Eastern Steam Navigation Company had run out of money and a new 'Great Ship Company' was formed, with the original shareholders (presumably including Brunel) getting back just 12.5% of their investment. The second company would struggle in its turn.

Brunel himself had succumbed to an illness diagnosed (by a Dr Bright) as Bright's disease, and was soon making long trips to warmer climes for health reasons. He was probably totally worn out by the stresses of the building and launch of the *Great Eastern*. The ship had to be fitted out under John Scott Russell's supervision. Brunel returned to Britain to inspect her before she left her moorings, and suffered a stroke while on board. He remained conscious, at home, waiting for news of the maiden voyage.

The news was not good. As she was passing Dungeness there was a huge explosion; six men died and others were injured. The cause seems to have been a muddled command structure, with neither Russell's men nor the crew knowing who was responsible for opening a valve at the appropriate time. Brunel died a week later.

Commercially the *Great Eastern* was a failure, her building and launch having effectively ruined two companies. She was simply too big, having been specifically designed for travelling to the Far East and Australia; there was insufficient business to be had, and she could not compete effectively in the Atlantic trade. A use was later found for her, laying submarine telegraph cables.

The Clifton Suspension Bridge is seen as one of Brunel's great achievements, but see page 11 for a slightly different perspective

The achievement

IKB was a visionary engineer quite often way ahead of his time, for example the SS *Great Eastern* had a double-skinned hull – decades ahead of its use in any other vessel but now seen as essential. On the other hand he was not omniscient. It's a shame that the devotee of the atmospheric system should have dismissed early electrical machines, saying they should be 'considered as toys'. In time electric traction would provide the answer he had sought.

The traditional role of the engineer was to be told by a company or a public body what was needed, and then to produce the best possible solution – 'best' meaning within financial limits as well as in its technology. IKB didn't need to wait and be told: he was capable of imagining things which nobody had hitherto thought of, and his powers of persuasion were such that company directors would often themselves be carried away by the possibilities.

Sometimes the projects would start with insufficient funds, and Brunel might well have underestimated the costs, often because he would improve on the design as the project proceeded. Add to that his often poor management ('too much of doing and undoing'), his having too many irons in the fire, hostility to teamwork and reluctance to delegate, and it is not surprising things sometimes went wrong.

But often they went right, even if not for the investors. His career may have had its ups and downs, and his personality was not always agreeable, but his legacy in the West Country has been profound, and there are places to see which embody the grandeur of his vision.

Some Brunel places to see

In Bristol

SS *Great Britain*
Clifton Suspension Bridge
Bristol docks
Temple Meads Station

In south Devon

Starcross
Torre engine house (photo below)
Watcombe Park (Brunel Woods)
Ivybridge viaduct

The railway bridge at Linketty Lane, Plympton, one of many hundreds of routine bridges Brunel designed for his railways

In Plymouth
Royal Albert Bridge
Plympton, Linketty Lane bridge

In Cornwall
Liskeard viaduct

Some books about Brunel

Derrick Beckett, *Brunel's Britain*, 1981
Steven Brindle, *Brunel: the man who built the world*, 2005
R Angus Buchanan, *Brunel: the life and times of Isambard Kingdom Brunel*, 2002
Adrian Vaughan, *Isambard Kingdom Brunel: Engineering knight-errant*, 1991
Isambard Brunel, *The Life of Isambard Kingdom Brunel, Civil Engineer*, 1870 (on-line)